COLOR MY OW

DINO STORY
2

AN IMMERSIVE, CUSTOMIZABLE COLORING BOOK FOR KIDS
(THAT RHYMES!)

BRIAN C HAILES

For information about permission to reproduce selections from this book, please write Permissions, Epic Edge Publishing, 1934 Fielding Hill Ln, Draper, UT 84020.

www.epicedgepublishing.com

Library of Congress Cataloging-in-Publication Data
Color My Own Dino Story 2: An Immersive, Customizable Coloring Book for Kids (That Rhymes!)
Written by Brian C Hailes

p. cm.
Summary: Travel back in time . . . again . . . to revisit your favorite prehistoric monsters that once ruled the ancient world, but this time, you'll run into a brand new grouping of formidable species that roamed the unstable plains, mountains and marshes! Powerful meat-eaters and peaceful herbivores roam this 3-in-1 coloring book, storybook, and interactive writing activity book. Color these beasts and their prehistoric habitats flush with trees, mountains, volcanoes and comets whizzing across the sky as you become immersed in your very own customizable tale. You will find many of the most popular dinosaur types as you traipse along—sometimes alone, and sometimes interacting with other dangerous giants! Buy this coloring book today and share in the fun, excitement and pure wonder of these tyrant lizards—with a special child for story time . . . and coloring time! This activity book is a great non-screen alternative to stimulate a kid's creativity and imagination. And it also makes a perfect gift!

(Intended for kids ages 6-12 . . . or all kids at heart)

1. Childrens—Fiction. 2. Childrens—Dinosaurs
3. Childrens—Coloring Books
II. Hailes, Brian C., ill. III. Title.

Paperback ISBN-13: 978-1-951374-43-3
Hardback ISBN-13: 978-1-951374-44-0

Printed in the USA
Designed by Epic Edge Publishing

10 9 8 7 6 5 4 3 2 1

Dig deep enough into your imaginations and you will find much more than bones!

— B.C. Hailes

COLOR MY OWN
DINO STORY
2

AN IMMERSIVE, CUSTOMIZABLE COLORING BOOK FOR KIDS
(THAT RHYMES!)

STARRING: _____

(your name)

Back to the land of the dinosaurs!

We return through time and space

To see these ancient beasts firsthand.

Be wary! It's a dangerous place.

My name is _____,
(your name)

And I study these "terrible lizards,"

That lived among the deserts, marshes,

Hot plains, mountains, blizzards . . .

Scelidosaurus

Stegosaurus

First, we find some _____,
(herbivores, plant-eaters or omnivores)

That like to eat the leaves,

And a stegosaur with a plated back,

With a tail as thick as trees.

My favorite is the _____,
(your favorite dinosaur)

Though it changes, win or lose;

The more I learn, the less I'm sure,

And it's often hard to choose.

Besides the dinosaurs, there are

The pterosaurs of the air!

They shriek and bite and flap and _____
(cry, screech or squeal)

From their high-up, cliff nest lairs.

Scaphognathus

Pteranodon

T hey fly on massive wings that

Stretch across the ancient sky;

And swoop to catch their prey,

_____ , pecking, 'til it dies.

And then, there are the armored ones

With their giant spikes and clubs;

Ankylosauria, as a _____ ,
(family, suborder or group)

Don't cuddle, and they don't like hugs.

They use those rock-hard _____
(weapons, armaments or defenses)

To protect themselves against

Some of the most threatening teeth and claws

Nature has ever dispensed!

Saichania

Diplodocus

A Diplodocus reaches the heights
Of some the highest tree-borne leaves,
And lumbers around with over twenty tons
Of _____ to move and heave.
(mass, fat or muscle)

It's size and whipping tail and neck
Are its only outer defenses,
But when smaller_____ attack,
(predators, carnivores or meat-eaters)
They'll likely regret the consequences!

My best friend, _____ ,
(your best friend's full name)
Has a different favorite than mine;
_____ likes the _____ ,
(He or She)   (your best friend's favorite dinosaur)
Of the _____ bloodline.
(that dinosaur's family or suborder)

Oviraptor

Saurolophus

I tend to like the _____ ones,
(bigger or smaller)

They're _____ formiddable;
(more or less)

It's not all about teeth or armor,

But whether they're more _____.
(indomitable or lovable)

I'm only _____ feet tall,
(your height)

But bigger than Velociraptor.

(However, I wouldn't want to run into

A Utah Raptor, or try to be *its* captor)

Velociraptor

Utahraptor

Gorgosaurus

Gorgosaurus rears its head,

Its territory, marking.

Daring one and all to challenge;

On its domain, embarking.

Most—including us—back down,

_____ off into the greenery.
(Slinking, Crawling or Hiding)

Luckily, it's already fed,

And we blend into the scenery.

Yutyrannus

A Yutyrannis _____

(scavenges, munches on or picks at)

A carcass that's been dead,

But spots a Dimetrodon, with flesh

That's still as fresh as bread . . .

It growls a threatening _____,
(rumble, thunder or outburst)

And moves in for the attack.

In response, the spine-backed quadruped

Bares teeth, and bellows back!

Dimetrodon

A Woolly Mammoth tromps around,

With tusks of fourteen feet!

But still it eyes its predators,

Who'd love to _____ its meat.

(taste, eat or try)

Woolly Mammoth

Neovenatoridae

Plesiosaurus

To dive in Prehistoric depths,

Also proves a _____ thing;
(deadly, risky or lively)

Hungry swimming creatures search

For game on which to spring!

The Plesiosaurus, with its

Sleek and streamlined tail and fins,

Is no exception; it moves faster

Than a _____ , and it spins!
(Great White, Killer Whale or Giant Squid)

Who do you think would win?

The Tuojiangosaur or the Teratophoneus?

_____
(your answer)

Tuojiangosaurus

Teratophoneus

At last, we come upon the King,

Tyrannosaurus Rex!

A _____ that commands a
(giant, monster, force or behemoth

Pant-wetting type of respect.

Tyrannosaurus Rex

Albertosaurus

It's not alone in that regard;
When Albertosaurus roars,
You flee every bit as fast to
Hiding places on all fours!

Dromaeosaurus

Charonosaurus

The journey's nearly cost our lives;

Surviving monsters is a thrill!

But living among these _____ beasts,
(amazing, awesome or marvelous)

It's surely run, kill or be killed!

With heavy, swiftly-pounding hearts,

We leave this long lost world;

Back to the future—again—through time,

_____ , space and dust, we're hurled!

(Light, Fire or Sparks)

Austroraptor

Mamenchisaurus

Daspletosaurus

Stegosaurus

THE END

Yutyrannus

OTHER "COLOR MY OWN" TITLES
NOW AVAILABLE!

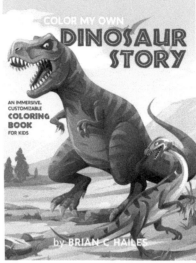

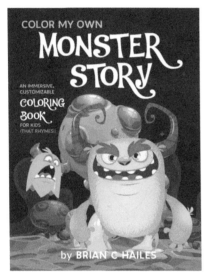

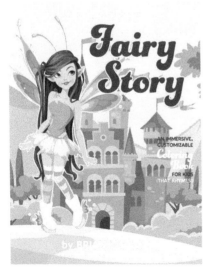

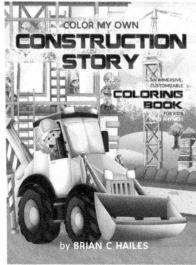

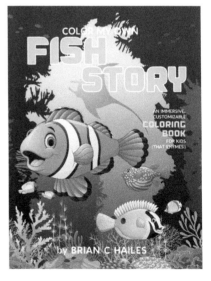

ABOUT THE AUTHOR

RIAN C HAILES, creator of Draw It With Me (www.drawitwithme.com), is also the award-winning writer/illustrator of over forty-five (and counting) novels, children's picture books, comics and graphic novels, including Blink: An Illustrated Spy Thriller Novel, Devil's Triangle, Dragon's Gait, Skeleton Play, Don't Go Near the Crocodile Ponds, If I Were a Spaceman, Here, There Be Monsters, Heroic, Passion & Spirit, Continuum (Arcana Studios), as well as McKenna, McKenna, Ready to Fly, and Grace & Sylvie: A Recipe for Family (American Girl), among others. In addition to his publishing credits, Hailes has also illustrated an extensive collection of fantasy, science fiction, and children's book covers as well as interior magazine illustrations. Hailes has received numerous awards for his works from across the country, including Winner of the L. Ron Hubbard Illustrators of the Future contest out of Hollywood. His artwork has also been featured in the 2017-2020 editions of Infected By Art.

Hailes studied illustration and graphic design at Utah State University where he received his Bachelor of Fine Arts degree, as well as the Academy of Art University in San Francisco.

He currently lives in Salt Lake City with his wife and four boys, where he continues to write, paint and draw regularly. More of his work can be seen at HailesArt.com

Other Titles Available from
Epic Edge Publishing

Illustrated Novels	Graphic Novels / Comics	Childrens Picture Books	Anthologies	Non-Fiction

Blink: An Illustrated Spy Thriller Novel
by Brian C Hailes

Devil's Triangle: The Complete Graphic Novel
by Brian C Hailes
& Blake Casselman

If I Were a Spaceman: A Rhyming Adventure Through the Cosmos
by Brian C Hailes
& Tithi Luadthong

Cresting the Sun: A Sci-fi / Fantasy Anthology Featuring 12 Award-Winning Short Stories
by Brian C Hailes,
Rick Bennett
& Nicholas Adams

Draw It With Me: The Dynamic Female Figure
(Available 2020!)
by Brian C Hailes

Avila
(Available 2021!)
by Robert J Defendi
& Brian C Hailes

Dragon's Gait
by Brian C Hailes

Here, There Be Monsters
by Brian C Hailes
& Tithi Luadthong

Don't Go Near the Crocodile Ponds
by Brian C Hailes

Heroic: Tales of the Extraordinary
by Blake Casselman,
David Farland,
Michael Stackpole
& more

DIWM 2020 Annual 1
(Available 2020!)
by Brian C Hailes,
Heather Edwards
& more

KamiKazi
by John English
& Brian C Hailes

Skeleton Play
by Brian C Hailes

Can We Be Friends?
by Edie New
& Cindy Hailes

Passion & Spirit: The Dance Quote Book
by Brian C Hailes

CPSIA information can be obtained
at www.ICGtesting.com
Printed in the USA
BVHW020354071220
594777BV00009B/90